CW00970268

Adapted from *Pride and Prejudice* by Jane Austen
Retold by Sarah Powell
Illustrations by Amanda Enright

Edited by Gemma Cooper • Designed by Claire Munday

Printed and bound in China, 0240617
10 9 8 7 6 5 4 3 2 1

Studio Press
An imprint of Kings Road Publishing
Part of Bonnier Publishing
The Plaza, 535 King's Road,
London, SW10 0SZ
www.studiopressbooks.co.uk
www.bonnierpublishing.co.uk

Pride & Prejudice

A Search & Find Book

Illustrated by Amanda Enright
Original story by Jane Austen • Retold by Sarah Powell

With an introduction by Annalie Talent, Jane Austen's House Museum

Jane Austen
1775-1817

Jane Austen was born in 1775 in Hampshire, England. She was one of eight children and although her parents weren't rich, Jane had a comfortable upbringing. At the age of seven, she was sent away to school with her sister, Cassandra.

When she was 11, Jane left school and returned home. She started writing short stories to entertain her family and friends, who must have listened eagerly to her funny tales. At about the age of 18 she began writing in earnest, although she had to wait until she was 35 before her first novel, *Sense and Sensibility*, was published.

Jane went on to have three more novels published in her lifetime, including her most famous story, *Pride and Prejudice.* Her works received good reviews and she was invited to dedicate one of her books, *Emma*, to the Prince Regent.

Jane Austen died in 1817 at the age of 41. She was not a well-known writer in her own lifetime, but her fame grew steadily in the years after her death. Today, her books are read worldwide and have been adapted many times for film and television. Jane Austen is now recognised as one of the greatest writers who ever lived.

Pride and Prejudice
1813

Pride and Prejudice is Jane Austen's most famous novel. She began writing it at the age of 20; at this stage, she called it *First Impressions.*

Jane shared her story with family and friends. Her father was so impressed that he tried to get it published, but Jane had to wait several years before she finally saw her book in print. By this time, she had revised the story and renamed it *Pride and Prejudice.* Jane was particularly fond of her book and referred to it as her 'darling child'. It was an instant success with the public.

Pride and Prejudice is a romantic comedy which follows a year in the life of Elizabeth Bennet (known to her friends as Lizzy). Lizzy is lively and funny, and prides herself on being a good judge of character. However, during the story, she learns the lesson that you can't always judge on first impressions.

Since its publication, readers have loved the book's humour, cast of varied characters and the growing relationship between Lizzy and Mr. Darcy. *Pride and Prejudice* is a story that can be enjoyed as much today as when it was first written over two hundred years ago.

Annalie Talent, Jane Austen's House Museum

Meet the Characters

There is a fascinating world of characters waiting to be discovered on the search and find pages. From the Bennets and their cousin Mr. Collins to Lizzy's friend Charlotte, eligible Mr. Bingley, and stern Mr. Darcy.

MR. BENNET

"Mr. Bennet was among the earliest of those who waited on Mr. Bingley. He had always intended to visit him, though to the last always assuring his wife that he should not go…"

MRS. BENNET

JANE BENNET

LIZZY BENNET

MARY BENNET

LYDIA BENNET

"To be fond of dancing was a certain step towards falling in love."

KITTY BENNET

"It is a truth universally acknowledged, that a single man in possession of a good fortune, must be in want of a wife."

"Bingley was sure of being liked wherever he appeared; Darcy was continually giving offence."

Welcome to Meryton

Where we meet …

Mr. Bingley arriving at Netherfield Hall,
Mr. Bennet visiting the new neighbour,
Mrs. Bennet hoping for a wedding,
Lydia Bennet the youngest and silliest,
Kitty Bennet a giggling daydreamer,
Mary Bennet ignoring her silly sisters,
Jane Bennet, quiet and good, and
Lizzy Bennet walking with her sister.

Search and find:

MR. DARCY

JANE BENNET

MR. BINGLEY

LYDIA BENNET

MRS. BENNET

KITTY BENNET

MR. BENNET

MARY BENNET

LIZZY BENNET

CHARLOTTE LUCAS

NETHERFIELD HALL
LONGBOURN

The Meryton Assembly

At which …

The new neighbours are introduced,
Jane is asked to dance by Mr. Bingley,
Mr. Bingley is enchanted by her beauty,
Mr. Darcy refuses to dance with Lizzy,
Lizzy overhears Mr. Darcy's insult,
An angry Lizzy tells her friend Charlotte,
Lydia and Kitty giggle all evening, and
Mary is praised for being accomplished.

Search and find:

A PROUD LIZZY

A GIGGLING LYDIA

A PRETTY JANE

A LAUGHING KITTY

A SHY MR. BINGLEY

A PRAISED MARY

A STERN MR. DARCY

A MERRY MRS. BENNET

A SNOOTY CAROLINE

A HAPPY CHARLOTTE

The Visit to Netherfield Hall

In which …

Jane is invited to visit on a rainy day,
A doctor is called to treat Jane's cold,
Mr. Bingley is concerned for poor Jane,
Lizzy rushes to Netherfield Hall,
Mr. and Mrs. Hurst act high-and-mighty,
Mr. Darcy begins to admire Lizzy,
Caroline Bingley becomes jealous, and
Mrs. Bennet arrives, and offends Darcy.

Search and find:

A POORLY JANE

A BORED MRS. HURST

A WINDSWEPT LIZZY

A SLEEPING MR. HURST

A SNOOTY MISS. BINGLEY

A LETTER FROM GEORGIANA DARCY

A WORRIED MR. BINGLEY

A DEPARTING DOCTOR

AN ADMIRING MR. DARCY

A PLAYFUL DOG

The Dinner with Mr. Collins

At which …

The Bennets' cousin, Mr. Collins, visits,
A good dinner is ordered for the evening,
Mr. Collins boasts about Lady Catherine,
Mr. Bennet declares him a silly man,
Mr. Collins announces he wants a wife,
Mrs. Bennet suggests Lizzy, not Jane,
Mr. Collins decides to marry Lizzy, and
Lizzy decides to avoid Mr. Collins.

Search and find:

TWO BLUE BIRDS

A HUNGRY FOOTMAN

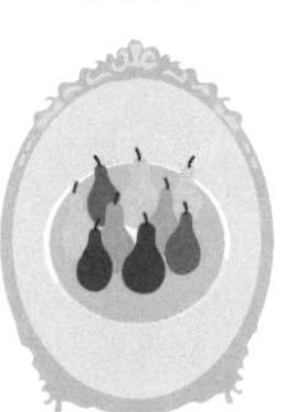

A DISH OF PEARS

A PATIENT CAT

A NAUGHTY DOG

A LOST RIBBON

A SCURRYING MOUSE

FIVE SILVER SPOONS

FIVE YOUNG SISTERS

A VERY LONG BOOK

The Trip into Meryton

In which …

The Bennet sisters visit the shops,
Mr. Collins decides to accompany them,
The dashing Mr. Wickham is introduced,
Jane unexpectedly meets Mr. Bingley,
Mr. Darcy is rude to Mr. Wickham,
Wickham tells Lizzy a troubling secret,
Mr. Bingley announces a grand ball, and
Mr. Collins asks Lizzy for the first dance.

Search and find:

A CHARMING MR. WICKHAM

A SHY JANE

A CROSS MR. DARCY

A CHATTY KITTY

A BASHFUL LIZZY

A BORED MARY

A FLIRTY LYDIA

A STAMMERING BINGLEY

A BAG OF CHERRY-PINK RIBBONS

A HURRYING CHARLOTTE LUCAS

The Grand Netherfield Ball

In which …

Jane dances with Mr. Bingley,
Mr. Collins acts ridiculously,
Lizzy avoids lovestruck Mr. Collins,
Poor Mary sings out of tune,
Caroline Bingley appears very bored,
Mr. Darcy asks Lizzy to dance,
Lizzy says she met Mr. Wickham, and
Mr. Darcy and Lizzy quarrel.

Search and find:

A DANCING JANE

A LAUGHING KITTY

A ROMANTIC MR. BINGLEY

A SINGING MARY

AN UPSET LIZZY

A SILENT MR. DARCY

A FRIENDLY CHARLOTTE

A SILLY MR. COLLINS

A GIGGLING LYDIA

A BORED CAROLINE BINGLEY

The Proposal from Mr. Collins

In which …

Mr. Collins insists on marrying Lizzy,
Lizzy refuses him, many times,
Mrs. Bennet is overcome with despair,
A determined Lizzy faces her parents,
Mr. Bennet agrees with Lizzy,
Jane receives a letter with sad news,
Mr. Bingley is leaving for London, and
Mr. Collins proposes to Charlotte.

Search and find:

AN ARROGANT MR. COLLINS

A BOOK OF MUSIC

A SURPRISED CHARLOTTE

A DISAPPOINTED JANE

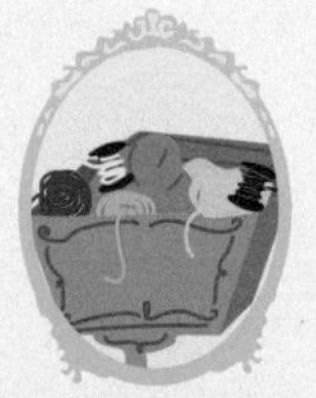

A BUNDLE OF SEWING

A PLATE OF HOT CRUMPETS

A WRITING BOX

AN OLD HAT

AN INVITATION FOR JANE

A DEPARTING BINGLEY & DARCY

The Trip to London

In which …

Jane stays in London with the Gardiners,
A letter is written to the Bingleys,
Jane writes to Lizzy with news,
Mr. Collins and Charlotte are married,
Caroline Bingley finally visits Jane,
Jane hopes to hear news of Mr. Bingley,
Caroline hints that he loves another, and
Jane is left broken-hearted.

Search and find:

A WAITING JANE

A RUSHING AUNT GARDINER

A VISITING MISS. BINGLEY

A BUSY BUTLER

A FORLORN MR. BINGLEY

A SCURRYING MAID

A STERN MR. DARCY

AN ARRIVING POSTBOY

A LETTER TO LIZZY

A LAUGHING UNCLE GARDINER

The Visit to Hunsford

In which …

Lizzy visits Charlotte and Mr. Collins,
An invitation arrives from Rosings Park,
Mr. Darcy visits his aunt, Lady Catherine,
Lizzy and Mr. Darcy meet again,
Mr. Darcy suddenly proposes to Lizzy,
Lizzy learns Darcy took Bingley away,
A shocked Lizzy refuses Darcy's offer, and
Lizzy learns the truth about Wickham.

Search and find:

A DEPARTING DARCY

A TALKATIVE MR. COLLINS

A THOUGHTFUL LIZZY

A BUSY CHARLOTTE

A LETTER FROM JANE

AN AMUSED COLONEL FITZWILLIAM

A DISAGREEABLE LADY CATHERINE

ROSINGS PARK

A QUIET ANNE

A LETTER FROM MR. DARCY

The Holiday in Derbyshire

In which …

Lizzy travels with her aunt and uncle,
Many places and towns are visited,
Mr. Gardiner wishes to see Pemberley,
Lizzy is reluctant to visit the house,
Mrs. Reynolds takes them on a tour,
Lizzy unexpectedly meets Mr. Darcy,
Mr. Darcy invites them all to dinner, and
Lizzy wonders if she has been wrong.

Search and find:

A THOUGHTFUL LIZZY

A BUSY MRS. REYNOLDS

A PLEASED AUNT GARDINER

A SHY GEORGIANA DARCY

A CURIOUS UNCLE GARDINER

THE INN AT LAMBTON

A LETTER FROM JANE

PEMBERLEY HOUSE

A STARTLED MR. DARCY

MR. DARCY'S DOG, JULIUS CAESAR

The Visit to Pemberley

In which …

Lizzy and the Gardiners visit Pemberley,
Mr. Darcy introduces his sister,
Lizzy and Georgiana become friends,
Lizzy changes her opinion of Mr. Darcy,
An urgent letter arrives for Lizzy,
Lizzy must return home immediately,
Jane writes with terrible news, and
Lydia Bennet has run away.

Search and find:

A CURIOUS GEORGIANA

A SLEEPING DOG

A WELCOMING MR. DARCY

A SILENT LIZZY

A CHATTING AUNT GARDINER

A GRAND COLONEL FITZWILLIAM

A HAPPY UNCLE GARDINER

A STERN LADY CATHERINE

A PROUD MRS. REYNOLDS

A LETTER FROM JANE

The Search for Lydia

In which …

Lizzy learns Lydia left with Wickham,
Mr. Bennet looks for them in town,
Lizzy fears she'll never see Darcy again,
Mr. Gardiner joins the search,
Mrs. Bennet is frantic with worry,
The Bennets soon hear good news,
Lydia and Mr. Wickham are married, and
Lizzy discovers Mr. Darcy found Lydia.

Search and find:

A TROUBLESOME LYDIA

A DETERMINED MR. DARCY

A WICKED MR. WICKHAM

A SEARCHING COLONEL FORSTER

A WORRIED MR. BENNET

A LETTER TO MRS. BENNET

A QUESTIONING MR. GARDINER

A CARRIAGE TO LONDON

AN UPSET MRS. FORSTER

A RUNNING AWAY NOTE

The Unexpected Visitors

In which …

Mr. Bingley returns to Netherfield Hall,
Jane accepts his proposal of marriage,
The Bennets celebrate the engagement,
Lady Catherine arrives unexpectedly,
An argument about Mr. Darcy occurs,
Another unexpected visitor arrives,
Darcy proposes to Lizzy once more, and
Lizzy accepts, having fallen in love.

Search and find:

A LOVING MR. DARCY

A BASHFUL LIZZY

A DEPARTING LADY CATHERINE

A SLEEPING MAID

A HAPPY JANE

A SURPRISED MR. BENNET

A DISHEVELLED BUTLER

A GIGGLING KITTY

A CURIOUS MARY

A CONFUSED MRS. BENNET

The Wedding

At which …

Mr. Bingley marries Jane Bennet,
Mr. Darcy marries Lizzy Bennet,
Lady Catherine de Bourgh is unhappy,
Caroline Bingley pretends to be pleased,
Mr. Bennet is satisfied,
Mrs. Bennet is delighted,
Jane smiles with joy, and
Lizzy laughs with happiness.

Search and find:

A LAUGHING LIZZY

A PRETTY GEORGIANA DARCY

A HAPPY MR. DARCY

A PROUD MR. BENNET

A SMILING JANE

A GIGGLING KITTY

A BASHFUL MR. BINGLEY

AN UNHAPPY CAROLINE BINGLEY

A TEARFUL MRS. BENNET

A JOYFUL CHARLOTTE LUCAS

WELCOME TO MERYTON

THE MERYTON ASSEMBLY

THE VISIT TO NETHERFIELD HALL

THE DINNER WITH MR. COLLINS

THE TRIP INTO MERYTON

THE GRAND NETHERFIELD BALL

THE PROPOSAL FROM MR. COLLINS

THE TRIP TO LONDON

THE VISIT TO HUNSFORD

THE HOLIDAY IN DERBYSHIRE

THE VISIT TO PEMBERLEY

THE SEARCH FOR LYDIA

THE UNEXPECTED VISITORS

THE WEDDING